C000151551

KS2

VISUAL REVISION GUIDE

SUCCESS

QUESTIONS & ANSWERS

ICT

Author

Maxine Pountney

CONTENTS

WP, DTP AND GRAPHICS

MULTIMEDIA

WWW AND EMAIL

DATABASES & SPREADSHEETS

Revised

MODELLING

Revised

CONTROL AND MONITORING

Revised

TEST, ANSWERS AND USEFUL WORDS

Revised

FIRM FOUNDATIONS

THE COMPUTER

Name these computer parts.

1   **2**   **3**

4   **5**   **6**

7   **8**

Now answer these questions.

9 Numbers 1 to 6 combined are called computer _____ .

10 Numbers 7 and 8 are used for _____ .

Hi! I'm Mel. My friends say I'm a 'techie'?

And I'm Sam. My sister is 'teching-in' all the limelight probably!

★ **top tip** ★

IT is not just about using computers – there are other technical devices and equipment that are used to communicate information. It's important to learn what to use and when to use it.

THE KEYBOARD

Write down what these keys are and what numbers 4 to 9 are used for.

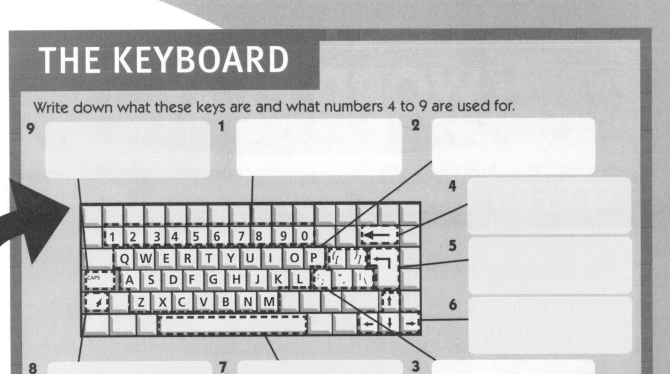

9 |
1 |
2 |
4 |
5 |
6 |
8 |
7 |
3 |

ICT EQUIPMENT

These devices are all examples of ICT hardware or software. What are they?

1 |
2 |
3 |
4 |

5 |
6 |
7 |
8 |

ICT

What do the letters ICT stand for?

WORD PLAY

SCREEN SHORTCUTS

Here's a sample screen of a combined word processor and desk-top publishing program. The icons are shortcuts to WP and DTP tools. What can you do if you select them?

1   2   3   4

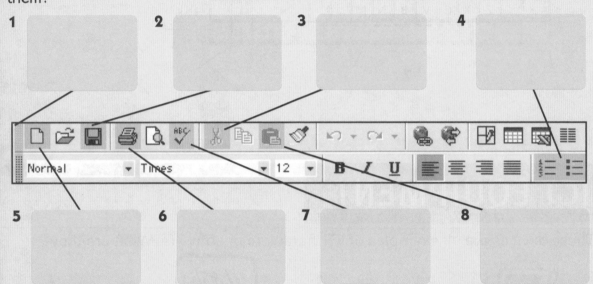

5   6   7   8

Have you ever tried keyboard shortcuts?

Is it a new hairstyle?

top tip

Keyboard shortcuts:
To CUT – Press CTRL and X.
To COPY – Press CTRL and C.
To PASTE – Press CTRL and V.
(Mac users use apple key instead of Ctrl)

AUTHOR'S ERRORS

This author typed his work first, then edited it later. He has used a thesaurus to find more interesting words and a spell-check to correct misspelt words. Which numbers show the spell-check corrections? Circle the words which show his use of the thesaurus.

Susan went into the room quickly. She wonted to see who had got there emily she had expected to sea, but Katy was allready here too so that was a good sign

Susan entered (1) the room quickly. She wanted (2) to see who had arrived. (3) Emily (4) she had expected to sea, but Katy was already (5) here too so that was a good sign! (6)

1 What has the author had to change at 4 & 6? _____
_____

2 What does the author have to do before he can change a word or group of words on a word processor? _____
_____

3 Which word is still wrong? _____
Explain why. _____
_____

ORDERED LISTS

1 These instructions for Cutting and Pasting are in the wrong order. Number them to put them in the right order.
To move text on a screen:

a Move the cursor to the place where you want to paste the text.

b From the Edit menu click PASTE.

c From the Edit menu click CUT.

d Highlight the text you want to move.

2 Which tools can you use to make lists? _____
_____

7

PAGE DEFINITION

MORE SCREEN SHORTCUTS

Here are some more icons that are shortcuts to WP and DTP tools.

What are they used for?

1

2

3

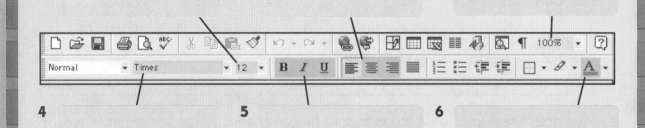

4

5

6

BETTER LETTERS

Sam has used WP and DTP tools to lay out his letter correctly. What has he done to each of these sections to produce the correct layout?

1

Sam Laptop
19 Station Road
Little Marsh
23rd July 2003

2

Dear Mr Madden,

Thank you for coming to our school last week. I really enjoyed your talk about the Wetlands.

3

I am really looking forward to coming to see the Wetlands during the school holidays.

4

Yours sincerely,
Sam Laptop

5 What key should Sam use to correct mistakes as he types? _____

6 What else should Sam do regularly as he types? _____

WHAT'S CHANGED?

DTP tools are used to make some bits of text stand out and look more important than others. Tick what's changed on these notices.

| stop |
| stop |

| go |
| go |

| go |
| go |

1 **a** colour & font ☐
   b font & size ☐
   c size & colour ☐

2 **a** colour & font ☐
   b font & size ☐
   c size & colour ☐

3 **a** colour & font ☐
   b font & size ☐
   c colour, font & size ☐

ADDING CLIP ART

Complete these instructions for adding a picture from the computer's Clip Art Gallery.

> select   layout   clip art   formatting   insert   search   click

1 Choose Picture from the _____ menu.

2 Choose _____ from the sub-menu.

3 _____ the Clip Art Gallery for a suitable picture.

4 _____ on picture to _____ and Insert it.

5 To be able to move or resize the picture, it needs _____. To do this, select the picture, right click the mouse, choose Format picture then select an option from _____ menu box.

I've got a great new CD with hundreds of clip art pictures on it.

How many pictures of clips do you need?

★ **top tip**
Look at lots of examples of posters and newspapers to see how they have used DTP and WP tools for different audiences.

TOOLBAR CHALLENGE

What are these tools used for?

1

2

3

4

5

6

7

8

9

10

11

12

THE ARTISTIC TOUCH

IMAGINATIVE GRAPHICS

Complete these sentences.

1 Pictures drawn on a computer are called _____ or _____.

2 This type of pattern is called a

_____ pattern. It is made by

using _____ and

_____ to duplicate the

original drawing.

3 This drawing is _____.

It is made using _____ and

_____ to duplicate the

original drawing and then using flip to

make it _____.

ARTIST AT WORK

Which tools have been used to make these shapes?

1

2

3

4

top tip
Use WORD ART to make some interesting text graphics. Have a play!

CREATIVE CROSSWORD

WORD ART

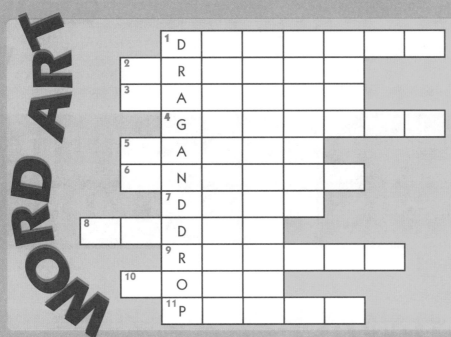

1 D
2 R
3 A
4 G
5 A
6 N
7 D
8 D
9 R
10 O
11 P

1 Drawing and graphics programs can use images from this type of camera.
2 Use the drawing tools to create pictures in the style of a famous ___.
3 A good graphics program will let you draw images on different ___
4 Another name for an image.
5 Use the ___ tools to create a picture.
6 The computer name that means to add something to a screen.
7 You can do this with the brush, spray, pencil or line tool.
8 A plan that is drawn on a computer is called a graphic ___.
9 To make something bigger or smaller.
10 A masthead of a newspaper or a school badge might need one of these.
11 When moving a picture or part of a picture on a page you can drag and drop, or cut and ___ or copy and ___.

11

INTERVIEWS

You have been asked to interview the local lollipop lady, a farmer, a shopkeeper and a policeman for the school magazine.

Think of at least eight questions for each person. Here are some to start you off.

- How long have you been a lollipop lady?

- What do you enjoy most about your job?

- What do you dislike about your job?

- What do you have to wear?

Type the questions on the computer. Which tools will you use to make the list? How will you keep notes of the interviews?

What other material could you collect during the interview that you might add later to your presentation?
(clue: it could involve a camera!)

BE A REPORTER INVESTIGATION

DESCRIPTIONS

Using a computer, write up each interview from your notes. Think about your readers and what they would like to know.

Which program will you use? Which tools will you use to make your work look attractive? How will you save your work? Did you take any photos during the interview that you can add now? Perhaps you could use Clip Art if you don't have any photos.

BOOKLET

The people you interviewed would like a copy of your work, so you decide to put all the interviews together in a small booklet. Design an interesting front cover using your drawing skills and some computer tools.

Compose and write a letter to send with the booklet, thanking each person for their help. To be a reporter you certainly need all your WP and DTP skills!

SCHOOL MAG

I'd like to be a policeman when I grow up.

Well you've had plenty of practice at tall stories!

top tip

Add special effects to your writing by using WORD ART, or by creating your own illustrations using the drawing tools.

CDs RULE!

CD SENTENCES

Underline the correct phrase to complete these sentences.

1 A CD is   a piece of hardware / something you plug into your computer / a disc that can save and store information.

2 To find information on a CD-ROM   use the Menu / read the instructions on the box / look on all the pages.

3 CD-ROMs store   text pages only / full length films / individual pieces of text, sound, still pictures, video and animation.

4 CD-ROMs can store   small amounts of information / huge amounts of information.

CD SEARCH

This word search contains 10 different things that are stored or saved on CD-ROMs. How many can you find?

VIDEOCLIPS

PHOTOS

ENCYCLOPEDIA

DICTIONARY

MUSIC

SOUNDS

GAME

CLIPART

FILES

IMAGES

G	A	M	E	S	O	P	E	H	D
T	P	S	E	I	N	H	N	C	C
Y	R	A	N	O	I	T	C	I	D
Y	H	F	M	N	N	I	Y	S	I
C	S	O	U	N	D	S	C	U	C
T	S	A	S	U	U	U	L	M	Y
R	E	R	V	S	O	T	O	H	P
G	G	Y	D	M	S	M	P	D	T
A	A	E	E	F	I	L	E	S	R
M	M	M	O	I	F	I	D	V	E
V	I	D	E	O	C	L	I	P	S
L	C	L	C	L	I	P	A	R	T

BUTTONS AND LINKS

The pages on a CD-ROM are linked together by hyperlinks. These appear on the page as buttons or images. Buttons or images can also link you to special effects or computer applications. Where do you think these hyperlinks lead to?

1

2

3

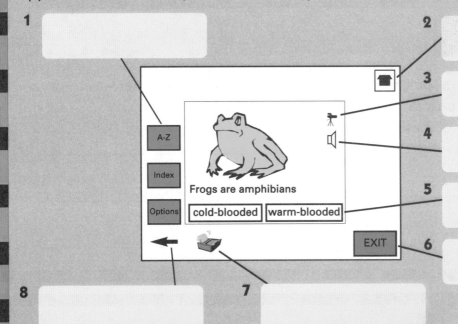

4

5

6

7

8

WHAT'S IN A NAME?

CD-ROMs are pre-recorded with information, but what does CD-ROM stand for?

a Compact Disk – Remember Our Menus

b Compact Disk – Read Only Memory

c Computer Disk – Read Only Menus

top tip
You can save or record information onto CD-ROMs using a CD-Writer, but once it has been written it can't be altered.

You can save or record information onto a CD-ROM using a CD-Writer, but once it has been written it can't be altered.

My English homework is a bit like that!

WEB WORKS

SOUNDS

1 Most computers have some simple recording software built in, but you need to attach one of these to many computers record sounds. What is it?

_____

2 Can you think of another way to get a sound file?

_____

_____

_____

PICTURES

Tick which of these can be used to import still or moving pictures into a multimedia page such as a web page or a presentation slide. (To import means to be able to bring graphics into a computer document.

1 digital camera ☐

2 sound recorder ☐

3 scanner ☐

4 printer ☐

5 keyboard ☐

6 Internet ☐

7 CD-ROM ☐

8 digital video ☐

9 monitor ☐

10 Clip Art ☐

top tip

If you are using a hand-held microphone to record sound, don't hold it too close to your mouth and point it away from the speakers.

I've added a running commentary to my presentation.

Is it wearing trainers?

WHAT'S ON A WEB PAGE?

Can you identify these features found on a web page?

1

2

3

4

5

LINKING IT TOGETHER

Underline the correct wording.

1 These are examples of (hyperlinks, sounds, videos).

<u>HOME</u>   <u>links</u>   <u>contact</u>   <u>pictures</u>

2 Hyperlinks and hypertext link (one word, one page, one picture) with another.

3 Navigating a site means (reading it, planning it, finding your way around it).

4 Home Page links and menu buttons are used as (navigation buttons, pictures to make a page look good).

5 Every page should have a link to (another website, a picture, the Home Page).

6 When planning some web pages, it is best done first on (the computer, on paper, in your head) with all the links showing.

7 Many web pages are a good examples of multimedia, because (they use text, animation, sound and video; you can listen to them; they give you lots of information).

SLIDE SHOW

SLIDE SORTER

Mel has made some slides about her visit to the market. She has included sounds, video clips and photos but now she needs to put the slides in the right order. Can you help her put them in the right order?

_____ , _____ , _____ , _____ , _____

1

Mrs Tulip

Next we went to Mrs Tulip's flower stall. We bought some daffodils.

Click on the picture to see Mrs Tulip selling her flowers

2

The market stalls

Here are the stalls we visited.

Click on the pictures to hear some of the market sounds

3

Mr Green

First we went to Mr Green's fruit and veg stall. We brought oranges, apples and pears.

Click on the picture to see Mr Green selling his fruit.

4

Picture gallery

We had a lovely day at the market.

Did you enjoy listening to our sounds and seeing our memories?

5

My visit to the market

By Mel

SPECIAL EFFECTS

Use the clues to find some special effects that make a presentation or a multimedia page more interesting.

1 A short movie.

2 Taken with a digital camera.

3 the technique of making objects or text move.

4 An added sound – it may be a special sound.

5 A still image.

6 Red, blue, green, etc.

TRUE OR FALSE?

Write down whether these statements are true or false.

1 Presentation software lets you use different fonts and coloured text. _____

2 Presentation software lets you use animation for pictures and text. _____

3 It isn't possible to change the order in which the slides appear. _____

4 When planning a presentation it is useful to create a storyboard of slides. _____

5 When planning a presentation you shouldn't think about the needs of your audience. _____

top tip
To end a slide show at any time press the Escape key.

I'm going to put everything I know about the Vikings in my presentation.

You were only thinking of doing two slides then!

19

BE A HISTORIAN INVESTIGATION

PREPARE YOUR TALK

As a local historian, you have been asked to give a presentation to a Year 5 class, who are just about to start a new project: Ancient Egypt.

Use these slides as a starting point for a presentation.

Add text, images, sound clips, video clips – and maybe some hieroglyphics!

To keep your audience interested, animate some of the slides – maybe you could have the gods 'appearing' on the screen one at a time with some sound clips added for special effect!

Make some notes:

_____

_____

_____

_____

_____

top tip
A presentation looks better when all the slides are presented in the same style. That means using the same colour scheme on each page.

Do you wish you could travel back in time?

As long as I was back in time for tea!

SLIDE SHOW

Change the order and the headings to match what you want to say. You're the historian, so it's over to you. Use the pointers to help you and get going!

- the culture
- the people
- the capitol

ANCIENT EGYPT

THE PYRAMIDS

- their age
- their construction
- their purpose

EGYPTIAN GODS

- who they were
- what they symbolised
- how they were worshiped

MUMMIES

- religious practices
- mummification

FAMOUS PHARAOHS

- their power struggle
- life as a god

CONNECTIONS

TOOLBAR CHALLENGE

Here are some icons that you can see on the pages of your browser when you're connected to the World Wide Web. What are they used for?

1

2

3

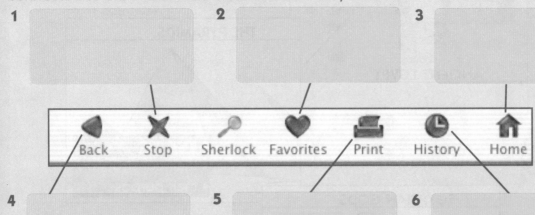

Back   Stop   Sherlock   Favorites   Print   History   Home

4

5

6

ADDRESS TEST

Use the words and the illustration below to fill in the gaps. Some words/phrases are used more than once.

| web page | www | World Wide Web | web address | URL | site | accurately |

🌐 www.lettsed.co.uk

This is a _____ _____. It is also called a Universal Resource Locator or _____ for short. Every _____ _____ has its own _____ _____, even pages on the same web _____! The address is like a code and it must be typed _____ without any errors and spaces. You don't need to type http:// but you must type _____ if it is part of the address. _____ stands for _____ _____ _____.

QUESTION AND ANSWER MATCH

Draw a line to match the answer to the question.

3 How do you make a search more accurate?

d A special web site that helps you to find links to other pages.

b No. None of them recognise 'and' or 'the' except one called Ask Jeeves.

c Type the most important key words in the search box and click GO or search.

1 What is a search engine?

4 Do you have to type sentences in a search box?

a Use + or the words AND or OR between key words.

2 How do you use a search engine?

top tip

Add any websites you find helpful to your Favourites or Bookmarks list. To add a site, choose Add from the Favourites menu and click OK.

I typed sheep + kangaroo in the Search Box.

Did you find any woolly jumpers?

QUICK WORD

electronic   mailbox   computer   Internet   telephone line
@   name   modem

Email is a quick and easy way to send messages using a _____.

To send and receive email the computer needs a _____.

To send and receive messages the computer needs to be connected to a

_____ and the _____. An Email address has two

parts. The first part of the address is the_____ of a person, a group or a code

name. The second part says where the person's_____ is.

The two parts are separated by the _____. This is all the mailbox needs to know

to send a message. Email is short for _____ mail.

WHAT'S IN THE BOX?

Email is sent and received via a mailbox. Write down in the spaces how each bit works.

1

2

3

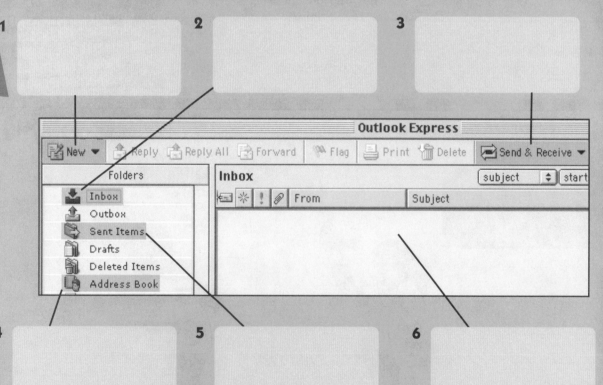

4

5

6

MAKING CONTACT

GETTING ATTACHED

Circle the things that you can attach to an email.

```
                    Email
        ┌──────┬──────┼──────┬──────┐
   Video clip  Paper  Photo  Sound clip  Text file
```

TEXTING

Some people use text messaging language to write emails because it's quicker. Can you work out what this person is trying to say?

THX 4 the EMA. WILL THNK ABT GNG 2 CINMA 2NITE. LT U KNW ASAP. CU SOON

1 It says: _____

_____

_____

2 When might you use this type of text? _____

3 When would you use proper words? _____

I've just got a text message, but I don't understand it.

You've got your phone upside down!

top tip
Most mailboxes have spell checkers – some let you use different fonts and coloured text as well!

BE A DETECTIVE INVESTIGATION

ON THE TRAIL

You are an internet detective. Your task is to find a place in the UK where an unusual event takes place each year. There are five letters in the place name and four clues to help you work them out. The first clue is in this box.

Yahooligans is a search engine that can help you search for the answers to the clues. You can find the search engine at www.yahooligans.com. Remember to use 'key words' from each clue as part of your search.

1st letter – Clue: The name of the place starts with the same letter as a popular 'citrus fruit'. The letter is _____

IT'S A BIT HARDER THIS TIME

2nd and 3rd letters – Clue: To find these letters you need to use the initials of a famous Scottish 'Loch' – does it have a 'monster' I wonder?

The letter is _____

3RD CLUE

4th letter – Clue: This letter matches the second letter of a famous 'English King' in fact there were eight kings with this name and this one had six wives!

The letter is _____

AND FINALLY...

5th letter – Clue: the last letter is the same as first letter of the search engine found at www.yahooligans.com.

The letter is _____

You should now have all five letters. Put them together.

_____ _____ _____ _____ _____

Find the place using a search engine and find out what's going on – but watch out for frying pans! Can you find out when this event was first held in England and why?

Make up some searches for your friends to try.

It's OK. They're microchips.

Sam, you're not supposed to eat while you're using the computer!

top tip
Use the key words to help you search. Put the most important word first.

27

RECORD IT

STORING INFORMATION

Complete the missing words.

A database is used to collect i_____. Information on a database is

organised into f_____ and r_____. Each f_____ on a r_____ is a

piece of information. A complete set of records is called a f_____. Data

entered into a database must be a_____. A Branching Database helps

you to s_____ and c_____ information by using simple questions that can be

answered with y_____ or n_____. A computer database lets you search for

information q_____.

MISSING FIELDS

Here's Mel's record about herself. It is taken from a file saved as 'Ourselves'.
What do you think fields 1–6 are?

Record 17:   **Ourselves**

1		Mel
2		girl
3		11
4		2/05/1992
5		blue
6		dancing, playing guitar

top tip

When creating a database, you can set the fields to accept only words or only numbers. It helps when you are filling in the records.

SEARCH AND SORT

Fill in the missing words – the answers are given in the picture below.

| Add new record | Delete record | View Sheet | List | Search | Sort | Save/print |

To look for information on a database, you need to _____ using key words. To put information into alphabetical order you can use _____.

To see all the records you can use _____ all. To see individual records you need to choose _____.

DECISION TREE

Here are some key words to use when creating a tree diagram or a branching database:

YES, NO, CLASSIFY, QUESTION, DECISION, ASK. Can you find them on the 'decision tree'?

GRID LOCK

TOOLBAR CHALLENGE

What are these?

1   2   3

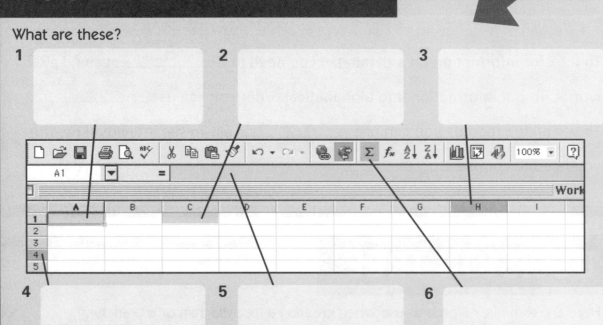

4   5   6

CELL REFERENCES

Use these cell references to read the story.

A3, C3, B5, B1, E2, A6, C5, E5, C1, A8, B3, D1, B2, A4, C7, D8, D5, A1, D2, B6, D6, A2, C2, E4, B7, A5, D4, E7, B8, E1, E3, B4, A7, C4, C8, C6, D7, E8, E6.

	A	B	C	D	E
1	numbers	a	into	rows.	numbers.
2	Spreadsheets	You	are	into	grid
3	A	and	spreadsheet		They
4	can	are	pretty	out	used
5	working	is	organises	or	data
6	that	a	at	spreadsheet.	!
7	also	for	type	drawing	problems
8	columns	with	good	words	graphs

FIND THE SUM

The formula bar shows the formula that has been typed into the active cell.

1 What number will appear in C7? _____.

| C7 | ▼ | = | =C1+C2+C3+C4+C5+C6 |

	A	B	C	D	E
1			2		
2			4		
3			8		
4			16		
5			32		
6			64		
7					

2 What would be an easier way to write this formula using the word SUM?

_____

_____

_____.

3 More number crunching! Look at the formula to work out the answer:

| C1 | ▼ | = | =A1*B1 |

	A	B	C
1	28	4	

| C1 | ▼ | = | =A1/B1 |

	A	B	C
1	28	4	

The answer in C1 = _____.   The answer in C1 = _____

WHICH GRAPH?

Write down which types of graphs need to be used. Choose from this list.

> bar charts   line graphs   column graphs   pie charts

1 _____, _____ or _____ can be used to compare information or data.

2 _____ can be used to show the changes in data when time is passing.

I've got a problem Mel – I haven't finished my spreadsheet story and I don't know where to put my bookmark!

??!!

top tip
A computer spreadsheet or database lets you experiment with different graph types using the data entered. See which looks best and choose one that shows the information most clearly.

A LOCAL NEED

A new fast food shop is opening in the area. The manager is hoping to sell sandwiches, as well as burgers and hot dogs. She has asked you to carry out some research among your friends to find out about the likes and dislikes of young people in the area.

BE A RESEARCHER INVESTIGATION

A SURVEY

Here are the results of your survey.

Name	Which type of fast food do you eat?	Favourite sandwich?	How many times do you have fast food each week?	Is it a good idea to have another fast food shop locally?
Maggie	fish & chips	cheese	2	no
Pete	burgers	ham	4	yes
Tim	sandwiches	ham	3	yes
Sally	sandwiches	egg	5	yes
Glenn	burgers	cheese	5	yes
Jade	burgers	tuna	3	yes
Robert	hot dogs	ham	4	yes
Evangeline	sandwiches	cheese	1	no
Autumn	burgers	cheese	3	yes
Mark	fish & chips	tuna	4	yes

CREATE A CHART

Put your results into a database or a spreadsheet.

A database lets you search and sort the information.

Create some charts using the database, to help you decide what to tell the shop manager.

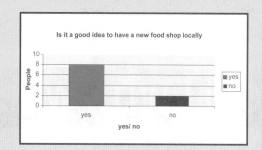

1 What is the average number of times people eat fast food each week?

_____

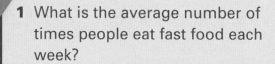

2 Which sandwich is the most popular?

_____

Extend the survey to include more people. Add the result to the database.

3 Why would it help your results to have more records?

_____

_____

_____

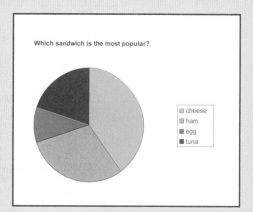

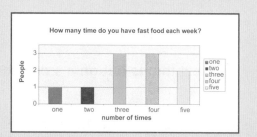

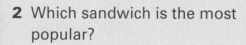

top tip
Watch out for spelling mistakes and errors with numbers when you enter and search for information.

Why don't you get hungry in the desert?

Because of all the sand – wich – that is there!

33

PREDICTIONS

MODEL WITH WORDS

Complete the crossword. All the answers are linked to computer modelling.

Across:

1 A computer model lets you experiment _____ (without danger)

2 To try or test things out on a small scale before building or doing the real thing.

6 This is a type of game with problems and puzzles to solve.

Down:

1 It may look or feel real, but it's a pretend or imaginary situation.

3 Playing an adventure, sporting or real life simulation.

4 The opposite of imaginary.

5 You can carry out one of these safely with computer simulation experiments.

Do you think I'd make a good model?

A model what?

WHAT'S MISSING?

difficult   imaginary   predict   experiments   impossible   real   dangerous

1 Computer simulations are used to show _____ or _____ situations.

2 A computer simulation lets you try things that would be _____ or _____ to do in real life.

3 A computer simulation lets you safely carry out _____ that might be very _____ to do in real life.

4 A computer simulation lets you _____ what you think will happen. It lets you try out your predictions and shows you what happens.

MODELS WITH NUMBERS

Spreadsheet models are investigations using numbers. Look at these questions, then write down your answers.

1 Spreadsheets use equations to perform calculations. What is a spreadsheet equation called? _____

C7	▼	=		
	A	B	C	D	E
1		length	breadth	area	perimeter
2	Shape X	6	2		
3	Shape Y	7	3		
4	Shape Z	8	4		

top tip
Remember all formulae begin with this: =

2 What formula would you type to calculate the area of Shape X?

_____

3 What formula would you type to calculate the perimeter of Shape X?

_____

4 How can you calculate the areas and perimeters of Shapes Y and Z without typing out the formula again?

_____

5 To investigate number patterns, you need to change the variables. In this spreadsheet what are the variables?

_____

BE A BUSINESS MANAGER INVESTIGATION

THE PROBLEM

As part of a school project you are asked to help out with a school magazine. You are in charge of 'the business' – the money!

It's your job to work out how much it will cost to print the magazine and decide which option is the best value for money. You want a reasonable number of pages for a reasonable cost.

SCHOOL MAG

THE COSTS

There is a sliding scale of costs per page

4 pages cost 10p per page

8 pages cost 9p per page

12 pages cost 7p per page

16 pages cost 6p per page

20 pages cost 3p per page

24 pages cost 3p per page

The magazine sells for £1.

There is a sliding scale of costs for binders

Costs to bind 4 pages 12p

Costs to bind 8 pages 12p

Costs to bind 12 pages 14p

Costs to bind 16 pages 15p

Costs to bind 20 pages18p

Costs to bind 24 pages 20p

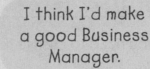

I think I'd make a good Business Manager.

But you can't even mind your own business!

SPREADSHEET

Add the number of pages to column A using the figures opposite.

Use a formula to calculate the cost of printing each magazine.

Use a formula to calculate the profit on each magazine.

The costs of printing a page and the cost of the binders have already been added for you.

	A	B	C	D	E	F	G
1							
2							
3	**School Business Plan**						
4							
5	Number of (p)	Cost per page (p)	Binder (p)	Total cost to print per magazine (p)	Profit per magazine pages		
6							
7		10	12				
8		9	12				
9		7	14				
10		6	15				
11		3	18				
12		3	20				

top tip

To calculate the cost per magazine, calculate (number of pages x cost per page) + cost of binder.

DECISIONS

Your results should look like this!

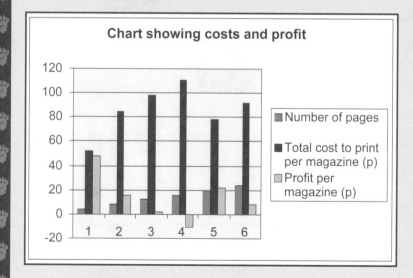

How many pages have you decided to put into your magazine? _____

Why?_____

_____

GIVING INSTRUCTION

THE BRAINS

The CPU is the 'brains' of the computer. It stores information; it receives messages; it sends out instructions.

Here is a diagram of a number of input and output devices that can be connected or used to send messages to the CPU.

Use the illustration and one of the following words to complete the sentences.

input   procedure   output

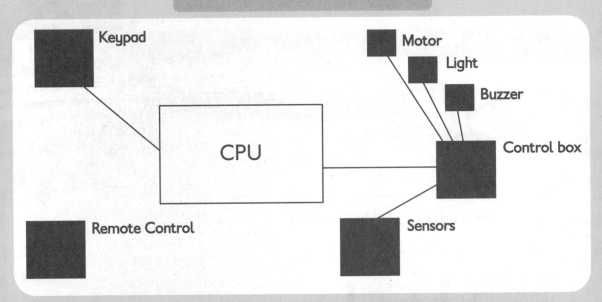

1 The keypad is an _____ device. It sends a message to the CPU when a button is pressed.

2 The remote control is an _____ device. It sends a message to the CPU when a button is pressed.

3 Sensors are _____. They send messages to the CPU via the control (interface) box when they detect something happening.

4 The CPU sends instructions to _____ devices such as lights, motors or buzzers via the control (interface) box after receiving instructions from the keypad or remote control.

5 A sequence of instructions is called a _____. The CPU stores procedures to make the equipment work properly.

BUS STOP CHALLENGE

Plan a route for the bus so that it visits every blue bus stop once, before it gets to the park. It cannot go on the same road twice. Use commands like Forward, Right and Left, plus the number of moves and degrees of turns. When writing down the moves, 1cm = 1 move, e.g. to move forward 10cm on the plan write forward 10.

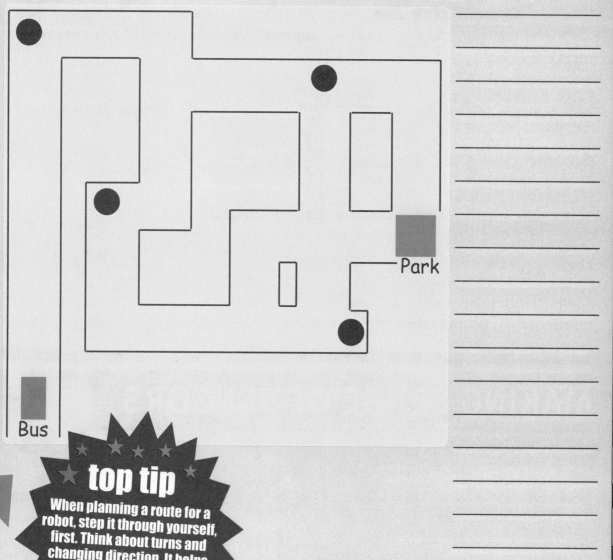

Park

Bus

top tip
When planning a route for a robot, step it through yourself, first. Think about turns and changing direction. It helps as well if you know the difference between left and right!

I think the bus should turn left.

It's a shame you haven't left with it - Ha ha!

WATCHFUL EYE

IN AND OUT

Use the illustration to show some of the input and output devices that you can connect to a control box.

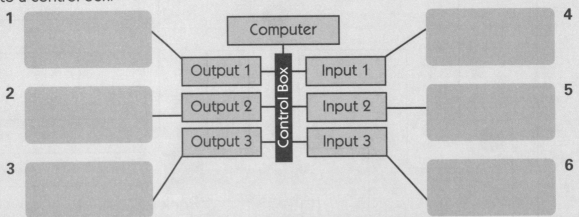

1

2

3

| Computer |

Output 1		Input 1
Output 2	Control Box	Input 2
Output 3		Input 3

4

5

6

7 Which input and output devices could be used to monitor the temperature in school for a 24-hour period? _____

MAKING SENSE OF SENSORS

Circle the true statements and cross out the false ones.

1 Sensors are used to monitor changes to the temperature, light or sound.

2 Sensors are input devices.

3 Sensors are output devices.

8 Control boxes can record data from sensors without being attached to a computer.

sensors

4 Computers can record changes detected by sensors over long and short periods of time.

7 A datalogger is a device that can record data from sensors without being connected to a computer.

5 Sensors can be useful for scientific experiments.

6 Light sensors record noise levels.

LOGO LANGUAGE

Logo has a language of commands that are used to control and drive floor and screen turtles. Here are some basic actions. Which commands do you type into the computer if you want your turtle to perform these?

Command short form	Command full word	Action
		turn right 90° clockwise
		turn left 90° anticlockwise
		turn right 120°
		forward
		back
		pen up
		pen down

TURTLE GRAPHICS

Screen turtles follow procedures for drawing shapes measured in 'screen turtle steps'. Using Logo, what procedure would you give the turtle to do the following?

1 Draw a square with sides 50. _____

2 Draw a square with sides 100 using the command 'repeat'. _____

3 Draw a pentagon with sides 90 using repeat. _____

4 What sort of picture would you draw if you had taught the turtle the word 'square' and you typed this: 36 [square, right 10]? _____

I sense we are almost at the end.

For once you are right!

41

ROBOT CONTROLLER INVESTIGATION

THE MISSION

You have been asked to accompany an expedition to the pyramids. Your job is to set up and monitor a robot exploration.

You will take with you:

- a programmable robot
- some devices to attach to the robot
- a control box
- a laptop computer.

Explain why you need a laptop computer.

_____

_____

If I had a robot, I'd program it to wash socks.

And if I had one, I'd program it to wash you!

ON SITE

The robot has to manoeuvre through some small passageways to find a chamber near the centre. It may pass through other chambers that are dark or that have shafts of light coming through. There may be obstacles on the way. Which of these devices do you think would be useful to attach to the robot? Why?

1 light sensor _____

2 buzzer _____

3 noise sensor _____

4 switch _____

5 heat sensor _____

6 video camera _____

Can you think of any others that you would use? _____

_____

_____

THE CONTROL BOX AND THE COMPUTER

The control box sends signals to the robot by radio link; the robot relays messages back in the same way. The control box is linked to the computer. What does the computer do?

_____

_____

_____

TEST PRACTICE

| File | Edit | View | Insert | Format | Font | Tools | Table | Window | Work | Help |

Look at the menu bar.

1 Which menu do you use to open a document? _____

2 Which menu contains Copy, Cut and Paste? _____

3 Where would you find the spell check and thesaurus? _____

4 Mel and Sam are having a summer party and want to write a letter to Gran and Grandad inviting them to come along. Put these in the correct order to say how they would use the computer.

a Write letter

b Choose new Blank Document

c Save

d Check layout

e Print

f Open a word processing program

g Save

h Save document as 'letter invitation'

i Check spelling

j Save

CORRECT ORDER: ___ ___ ___ ___ ___ ___ ___ ___ ___ ___

Mum says the children can invite some friends to the summer party. Here is their plan for the invitation. Now they need to make it look more exciting so they change the layout and style.

> Party Invitation
>
> You are invited to a party at 12 Street Lane on Saturday 29ᵗʰ July from 3pm to 6pm. I hope you can come.
>
> Mel & Sam
>
> RSVP by email

5   Tick the most appropriate heading:

a   Party Invitation (no change)   ☐

b   Party Invitation (smaller)   ☐

c   PARTY INVITATION (bigger, capital letters and in colour)   ☐

6   Tick the most appropriate layout:

a
> You are invited to a party at 12 Street Lane on Saturday 29ᵗʰ July from 3pm to 6pm. We hope you can come.

b
> You are invited to a party at
> 12 Street Lane on Saturday
> 29ᵗʰ July from 3pm to 6pm.
> We hope you can come.

c
> You are invited to a party at 12 Street Lane on Saturday 29ᵗʰ July from 3pm to 6pm. We hope you can come.

7   Which alignment has Mel chosen for 6b?

a   ☐   b   ▤ ☐   c   ▤ ☐

8   Which alignment has Sam chosen for 6a?

a   ▤ ☐   b   ☐   c   ☐

9   What else could they add to their invites to make them look more colourful? _____

Mel and Sam's friends reply by email. This is Mel and Sam's mail box. They have their friends' email addresses saved here.

```
New ▼ | Reply | Reply All | Forward | Flag | Print | Delete | Send & Re
        Folders          Inbox                            subject
   Inbox                 ✉ ❄ ! 🖉 From          Subject
   Outbox
   Sent Items
   Drafts
   Deleted Items
   Address Book
   Microsoft News Server
 ▷ Directory Services
```

10 Which box do they look in to check for new messages?

_____

11 How do they answer each message? _____

12 Mel hasn't heard from one of her friends and she wants to send an email. What should she do? _____

13 To get ready for the party Sam searches the Internet for some ideas. What does he use to help him search? _____

Search the Web: [   ] [Search] • Advanced
                                                  • Preferences

Sam types the word 'party' but the search engine finds hundreds of sites.

14 Mel suggests he improve his search by using one of these. Which one?

   a party AND game   ☐

   b find out about party games   ☐

   c party + games + children   ☐

While Sam is using the web, Mel plans the party food with mum.

15 Which computer program can help her budget for the cost and why?

_____

_____

This is the information she has put together so far.

	A	B	C	D	E	F
1	Party Budget					
2						
3		No. needed per guest	No. of guests	No. to buy	Cost per item	Total
4	Paper cups	1	25		0.08	
5	Paper plates	2	25		0.06	
6	Bread Rolls	2	25		0.12	
7	Cans of pop	2	25		0.35	
8	Box of eggs (6)		25	2	1.1	
9	Slices of ham		25	20	0.2	
10	Tins of tuna		25	4	0.65	
11	Small cakes	2	25		0.25	
12	Chocolate rolls	2	25		0.2	
13	Big pkts of biscuits		25	4	1.6	
14						
15				Grand Total		

16 Which formula will she use for D7? _____

17 Which formula will she use for F9? _____

18 There are three ways she can find the Grand Total in F15, but which two are the quickest? _____

19 How can she work out how much she is spending on each person?

_____

20 Mel has forgotten to add Gran and Grandad to her numbers.
She now has 27. Does Mel have to redo all her formulae? _____

Explain your answer _____

_____

21 Sam has a small robot. He thinks it would be a good idea to make a
robot Treasure Hunt as a party game. Here's his maze.

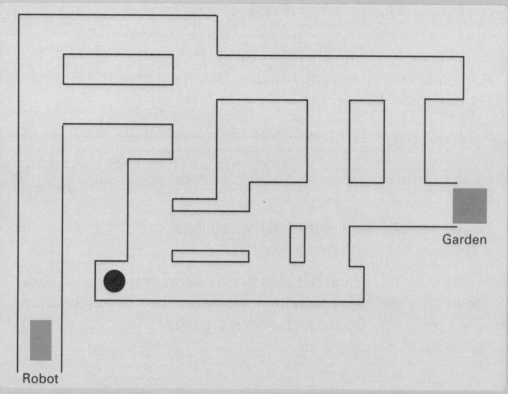

Garden

Robot

Sam has hidden a prize in the maze. Write down clear instructions for
the robot to find it and take it to the garden. The fastest person wins
the prize. (There are different routes – to use the shortest). When
writing down the moves, 1cm = 1 move, e.g. move forward 10cm on
the plan write forward 10.

_____

_____

22 During the party Mel records some video footage that she can
download onto the computer, while Sam takes photos using
a single-use camera. Which piece of equipment are they using:

a a digital camera and microphone ☐

b a digital video recorder and a camera with a film ☐

c a digital video recorder and a digital camera? ☐

23 If Sam wants to put his photos onto the computer when they are developed, what will he need to use?

    a printer ☐   **b** digital camera ☐   **c** scanner? ☐

Mel and Sam have a great time at the party and they have some wonderful photos and video to remind them of what they did. They would like to make something to give to their friends and to Gran and Grandad as well as a reminder of the party. It would include lots of clips and perhaps a message or two!

24 Which computer program will let them do this? _____

25 Why is this program a good one to use? _____

_____

26 How could they give a copy of what they have done to their friends? Think of three different ways.

    a _____

    b _____

    c _____

27 Finally, Mel and Sam write a thank you letter to Gran and Grandad – and one to Mum and Dad as well!

They write their letters first but then decide to make them look more interesting. The party was such fun – they want their letters to be fun too! Here are some shortcuts they use. What are they?

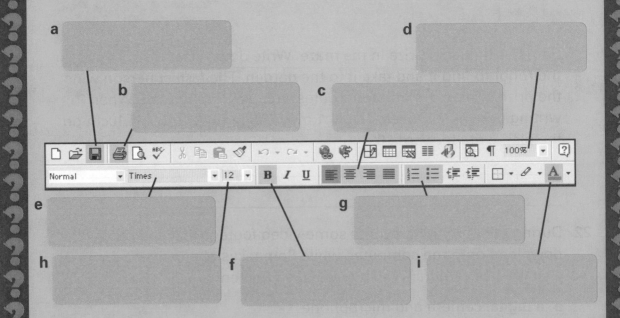

WP, DTP AND GRAPHICS

Pages 4–5
FIRM FOUNDATIONS

THE COMPUTER
1 Computer or power unit containing CPU. Sometimes tower-shaped and placed next to the screen, sometimes box-shaped and placed under the screen.
2 Screen or monitor.
3 Keyboard.
4 Printer.
5 Mouse.
6 Scanner
7 CDRom/DVD.
8 Floppy disk.
9 hardware
10 software

THE KEYBOARD
1 Number keys.
2 Letter keys.
3 Punctuation and symbol keys.
4 Backspace – moves the cursor back one space.
5 Enter – creates a new line (sometimes called a return key).
6 Cursor keys – moves the cursor around the screen.
7 Space bar.
8 Shift keys – used for individual capital letters or symbols on top half of keys.
9 Caps lock – used to create a string of capital letters.

ICT EQUIPMENT
1 Laptop computer.
2 Camera.
3 Mobile Phone.
4 CD-ROM/DVD
5 Video recorder.
6 Television.
7 Radio.
8 Calculator.

ICT
Information and Communication Technology.

Pages 6–7
WORD PLAY

SCREEN SHORTCUTS
1 Tool bar.
2 Save the document.
3 Cut highlighted words.
4 Bulleted or numbered list.
5 Create a new document.
6 Print.
7 Spell-check.
8 Paste something saved on the clipboard.

AUTHOR'S ERRORS
Thesaurus: 1 and 3.
Spell-check: 2 and 5.
1 The author changed the punctuation at 3 and 6.
2 Highlight it.
3 The word 'sea'. It is a correctly spelt word so the spell-check missed it but it is used in the wrong context.

ORDERED LISTS
1 The correct order for the instructions is: 1 = d; 2 = c; 3 = a; 4 = b.
2 Bullets and numbers.

Pages 8–9
PAGE DEFINITION

MORE SCREEN SHORTCUTS
1 Change size of text.
2 Align text left, right or centre.
3 Zoom.
4 Change font.
5 Bold, Italic or Underline text.
6 Change colour of text.

BETTER LETTERS
1 Enter key used at the end of each line to start a new line of the address. Text aligned using tab.
2 Text aligned left.
3 Used the Enter key twice to start a new paragraph and make an extra line space.
4 Centred text and used enter key.
5 The Backspace key.
6 Save his work.

WHAT'S CHANGED?
1 a
2 c
3 c

ADDING CLIP ART
1 insert
2 clip art
3 Search
4 Click; select
5 formatting; layout

Pages 10–11
THE ARTISTIC TOUCH

TOOLBAR CHALLENGE
1 Start shape.
2 Rubber.
3 Cropper (lets you pick up a colour and use it again in another part of the picture).
4 Pencil tool.
5 Spray can tool.
6 Straight line tool.
7 Flood fill tool.
8 Zoom.
9 Brush tool.
10 Text tool.
11 Curved line tool.
12 Shapes tool.

IMAGINATIVE GRAPHICS
1 images, graphics. (CGI's Computer Generated Images)
2 repeat. copy, paste.
3 Symmetrical. Copy, paste, symmetrical.

ARTIST AT WORK
1 Curved line.
2 Pencil line.
3 Shape and flood fill.
4 Shapes tool.

CREATIVE CROSSWORD
1 Digital.
2 Artist.
3 Layers.
4 Graphic.
5 Paint.
6 Insert.
7 Draw.
8 Model.
9 Resize.
10 Logo.
11 Paste.

WP, DTP AND GRAPHICS

Pages 12–13
BE A REPORTER INVESTIGATION

INTERVIEWS
Use bullets or numbers to make a list.
Use a digital camera to take photos to add to your document.

DESCRIPTIONS
Use a WP program to write up the interviews. DTP tools, digital photos or clip art will add interest to the text.
Use a digital camera to take photos to add to your document.

MULTIMEDIA

Pages 14–15
CD RULE!

CD SENTENCES
1 a disk that can save and store information.
2 use the Menu.
3 individual pieces of text, sound, still pictures, video and animation.
4 huge amounts of information.

CD SEARCH

BUTTONS AND LINKS
1 An A–Z index of key words.
2 The Home Page; this is usually the menu page.
3 A video clip.
4 A sound clip.
5 Another information page.
6 To stop using the CD-ROM.
7 The printer menu.
8 Back to the last page visited.

WHAT'S IN A NAME?
b Compact Disk – Read Only Memory.

Pages 16–17
WEB WORKS

SOUNDS
1 A microphone.
2 Download a sound file from a sound clip site; create a sound clip using online interactive music pages.

PICTURES
Digital camera, scanner, Internet, CD-ROM, digital video, Clip Art.

WHAT'S ON A WEB PAGE?
1 Banner.
2 Header.
3 Menu buttons – hyperlinks to other pages.
4 Hyperlinks to another website.
5 Link to Home Page.

LINKING IT TOGETHER
1 hyperlinks.
2 one page.
3 finding your way around it.
4 navigation buttons.
5 the Home Page.
6 on paper.
7 they use text, animation, sound and video.

Pages 18–19
SLIDE SHOW

SLIDE SORTER
5, 2, 3, 1, 4.

SPECIAL EFFECTS
1 Video clip.
2 Photo.
3 Animation.
4 Sound effect.
5 Clip Art.
6 Colour.

TRUE OR FALSE?
1 True.
2 True.
3 False.
4 True.
5 False.

WWW & EMAIL

Pages 22–23
CONNECTIONS

TOOLBAR CHALLENGE
1. Stop searching.
2. Quick link to your favourite websites.
3. Go back to your Home Page. This is the page you see every time you go online.
4. Takes you back to the last page you were looking at.
5. Print the whole page.
6. See all the pages you've visited.

ADDRESS TEST
web address
URL
web page
web address
site
accurately
www
www
world wide web.

QUESTION AND ANSWER MATCH
1 and d.
2 and c.
3 and a.
4 and b.

Pages 24–25
MAKING CONTACT

QUICK WORD
1. computer
2. modem
3. telephone line
4. internet
5. name
6. mailbox
7. @
8. electronic

WHAT'S IN THE BOX?
1. Click here to write a new message.
2. Click here to see messages received. Click on any messages to open them.
3. Click here to send a message that has been written.
4. Click here to open the address book to see any addresses you have saved.
5. Click here to read messages you have sent.
6. Read or write new messages here.

GETTING ATTACHED
All of these except paper.

TEXTING
1. Thanks for the e-mail. Will think about going to the cinema tonight. Let you know as soon as possible. See you soon.
2. In sending a SMS text message or e-mail to a friend.
3. When writing a letter or email in a more formal way.

Pages 26–27
BE A DETECTIVE INVESTIGATION
The citrus fruit is an **O**range
The Scottish loch is **L**och **N**ess
The English King is H**e**nry
The search engine is **Y**ahooligans
The place name is Olney and there is a pancake race held there every year. It has been held every year since1445. Nowadays there is also a race in Liberal, USA and the two towns compete for the fastest time.

DATABASES AND SPREADSHEETS

Pages 28–29
RECORD IT

STORING INFORMATION
information.
field, records.
field, record.
file.
accurate.
sort, classify, yes, no.
quickly.

MISSING FIELDS
1. Name.
2. Girl or boy / gender.
3. Age.
4. Date of birth.
5. Eye colour.
6. Hobbies.

SEARCH AND SORT
search.
sort.
list.
view Sheet/Record.

Decision Tree

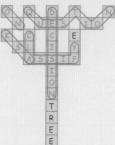

Pages 30–31
GRIDLOCK

TOOLBAR CHALLENGE
1. Active cell.
2. Cell.
3. Column.
4. Row.
5. Formula bar.
6. Autosum – a shortcut to adding a column or row of numbers.

DATABASES AND SPREADSHEETS

Pages 30–31 continued

CELL REFERENCES
1 A spreadsheet is a grid that organises data into columns and rows. You can type words or numbers into a spreadsheet. Spreadsheets are used for working out problems with numbers. They are also pretty good at drawing graphs!

FIND THE SUM
1 128
2 SUM(C1:C6)
3 7
4 112

WHICH GRAPH?
1 Bar chart, column graph or pie chart.
4 Line graph.

Pages 32–33

BE A RESEARCHER INVESTIGATION
1 3.4
2 Cheese
3 To reduce random fluctuations in the data.

MODELLING

Pages 34–35
PREDICTIONS

MODEL WITH WORDS
Across
1 safely   2 model   6 adventure
Down
1 simulation 3 game   4 real
5 test

WHAT'S MISSING
1 real, imaginary
2 difficult, impossible
3 experiments, dangerous
4 predict

MODELS WITH NUMBERS
1 Formula.
2 =B2*C2
3 2*(B2+C2) or 2*(B2:C2)
4 Copy and paste the area formula to D3 and D4. Copy and paste the perimeter formula to E3 and E4.
5 The length and the breadth.

CONTROL AND MONITORING

Pages 38–39
THE BRAINS

GIVING INSTRUCTION
1 input   2 input   3 input
4 output.   5 procedure.

BUS STOP CHALLENGE
forward 10
right 90
forward 4
right 90
forward 5
right 90
forward 1
left 90
forward 5
left 90
forward 6
left 90
forward 7
right 90
forward 2
right 90
forward 4

Pages 40–41
WATCHFUL EYE

IN AND OUT
Outputs: buzzer, light, motor.
Inputs: sensors – light, heat, sound.
7 Input – heat sensor.
  Output – light or buzzer.

MAKING SENSE OF SENSORS
True: 1, 2, 4, 5, 7.
False: 3, 6, 8.

LOGO LANGUAGE

Command, short form	Command, full word
rt 90	right 90
lt 90	left 90
rt 120	right 120
fd	forward
bk	back
pu	penup
pd	pendown

CONTROL AND MONITORING

Pages 40–41 continued

TURTLE GRAPHICS

1 forward 50, right 90, forward 50, right 90, forward 50, right 90, forward 50, right 90
2 repeat 4 [forward 100, right 90]
3 repeat 5 [forward 90, right 72]
4 A flower shape using 36 squares that overlap in a circular pattern.

Pages 42–43
ROBOT CONTROLLER INVESTIGATION

THE MISSION

You need the computer because you are controlling the robot.

ON SITE

1, 3, 5, 6.

All these can send information back to the computer to indicate where the robot is and what is happening inside the pyramid. The sensors indicate heat, light or noise. The video camera will let the controller detect obstacles to manoeuvre around. The level of noise may indicate whether the robot is in a small corridor or a large chamber.

THE CONTROL BOX AND THE COMPUTER

You type instructions (Commands) into the computer and these are sent to the robot via the control box. Signals from the robot are sent back to the control box, and you can monitor and record these using the computer.

REVISION TEST

Pages 44–48
TEST PRACTICE

1 File
2 Edit
3 Tools
4 f, b, h, a, c, d, g, i, j, e
5 c
6 b
7 b
8 c
9 Clip art or artwork
10 Inbox
11 Click on Reply
12 Click on Compose or Write message. She can find her friend's address in the address book.
13 A Search Engine
14 c
15 A spreadsheet because it can help her work out how much she is spending.
16 B7*C7
17 D9*E9
18 SUM(F4:F13) or Autosum
19 F15/C4
20 No, because the formulae haven't changed. The spreadsheet recalculates the total using the new figures and the formulae that Mel has typed in already.
21 fd8, rt90, fd5, r90, fd4, r90, fd1, lt90, fd3, r90, collect prize, rt180, fd6, lt90, fd2, rt90, fd4, enter garden
22 b
23 c
24 A presentation program such as PowerPoint.
25 It lets them use multimedia – they can put video, sound clips, photos and text on the pages.
26 Save it onto a floppy disk, save it onto a CD, attach it to an email.
27 a save a document/file
   b print
   c align left, right or centre
   d zoom – see the whole page
   e change the font
   f vbold
   g add bullets or numbers to a list
   h change the size of text
   i change the colour of the text

REALLY USEFUL WORDS

TECHNICAL TERMS

Data logging Using sensors to measure and record changes in temperature, light or sound over a long or short time.

File Collection of data saved with one name – for example, a text file, a sound file or a database file.

Images Pictures that appear on the computer screen that have been drawn using an art package, scanned from a scanner, copied from a CD-ROM or a web page, or downloaded from a digital camera.

Modem A piece of hardware inside a computer used to send and receive information via a telephone line.

Mouse Input device attached to a computer.

Multimedia A combination of words, sound, pictures and images – still and moving – controlled by a computer.

Procedures Structured commands used to control devices and equipment.

URL (Uniform Resource Locator) The name for a web address.

Word processor A computer program used for writing, editing, saving and printing words.

DISKS

CD-ROM (Compact Disk – Read Only Memory) Looks like a CD, but it contains words and graphics as well as sound. CD-ROMs store large amounts of information.

DVD (Digital Versatile Disk) Bigger and faster than a CD. It can hold full-length film video, still photos and computer data. Allows you to find and play back recorded multimedia.

Hard disk Found inside a computer. Used for storing large amounts of information.

Floppy disk Small portable disk that stores computer data and files.

HARDWARE

Control box A device with output and input sockets that connects to a computer. Instructions can be sent from the computer to the box to control lights, buzzers and motors plugged into the output sockets; instructions can be received by the computer through the box from sensors plugged into the input sockets.

Data logger A device with input sockets that can record data from sensors without being connected to a computer.

Digital camera A camera that stores the pictures it takes as digital pictures. These can be downloaded to a computer by a cable connection or a special floppy disk, then used in Graphics, DTP or Multimedia applications.

Floor turtle A floor robot that is controlled by Logo instructions sent from a computer. The turtle has a pen holder and can be programmed to draw shapes.

Hardware All the mechanical and electronic bits and pieces that make up a computer system, such as a keyboard or printer.

Keypad A touch-sensitive pad with letters, numbers or symbols. Keypads are found on some floor robots and electrical equipment. They are used to send instructions to the equipment.

Laptops Small rechargeable computers that are powered by batteries or run on electricity. Some are as powerful as a desk-top computer.

Palm-tops Small rechargeable hand-held computers powered by batteries.

Peripheral A device that can be plugged into a computer such as a disk drive, a printer or a scanner.

Roamer A floor robot that can be programmed to follow a sequence of commands.

Scanner A device that reads a paper image and sends that image to the computer so it can be seen on the screen. The screen image can be used by different software applications.

Screen turtle An on-screen robot used to carry out procedures to draw lines and shapes. Screen turtles respond to Logo instructions.

Sensor A device used to measure changes to light, temperature or sound. Sensors can be connected to control boxes or data-logging devices.

SOFTWARE AND APPLICATIONS

Adventure game A simulation program that involves a search or mission. Players solve clues or puzzles on the way and often collect 'objects' as part of their mission.

Computer program A set of instructions that make a computer perform a task.

Database Information that is organised and stored into fields and records. The information entered can be searched, retrieved and presented as lists or charts.

Desk-top publishing A computer application that helps you to change page layouts with graphics, images and words, in different sizes and styles.

Electronic mail (email) Mail that is sent and received using a modem in the computer which connects computers via a telephone line. The messages can contain words and/or graphics and attachment, such as sound or video clips.

Graphics Pictures or symbols on a computer screen that can be printed out or saved to disk. Also see Images.

Internet A worldwide network of computers that provides a huge source of information. The computers are linked through modems and phone lines.

Logo A programming language that gives instructions to a computer in words and numbers. It is used to control the movements of screen turtles.

Model A computer simulation of a real or imagined situation, with rules set by the computer. The software lets you change the rules to see the result of the changes on the computer screen.

Software A computer program.

Spreadsheet A computer program with cells on a grid. Spreadsheets can be used to model situations such as a tuck shop project or a maths investigation where numbers are involved. Cells can be linked by formulae so you can carry out calculations.